ESL
Worksheets and
Activities
for Kids

Table of Contents

Extras

There are just a couple of extras I want to let you know about before you start using this book.

Bounty for errors
If you find an error in this ebook, email me at:
miryung@eslconversationquestions.com

As a reward I will send you a free copy of any one of our ebooks. You can choose from one of these books:

ESL Role Plays: 50 Engaging Role Plays for ESL and EFL Classes

1,000 Conversation Questions: Designed for Use in the ESL or EFL Classroom

500 Grammar Based Conversation Questions

IELTS Study Guide: Quick Tips, Tricks, and Strategies

Join our reviewer program
We are always looking for qualified reviewers for our books. But we don't want to offer free review copies to just anyone. We want to offer them to people who are more likely to leave a review since they have left reviews in the past.

So if you have left a review of this book and are interested in receiving a free digital copy of one of our books as a review copy, let me know about your review and which book you are interested in at:

miryung@eslconversationquestions.com

We only ask that you actually review the review copy we send you. Once you write a review of the book we sent you, we can send you a digital review copy of another one of our books.

Thank you and enjoy the book!

Introduction

• What's in this book?

This book consists of 10 topics. Family, numbers, shapes, time, months, days, weather, prepositions, money, and animals. There are instructions for all of the worksheets at the beginning of each topic section. *Note to teachers: This book uses U.S. money for the money section.*

• What else is in this book?

At the back of the book there is an extra resource section with a mini-book template and flash cards for warm ups. There are also pictures of money that can be cut out and used for the money section. Students can use the money during class activities. There is also a book template which teachers can customize for any topic.

• Why are there no page numbers?

The pages in this book are meant to be reproduced and given to students. There are no page numbers so that when you print out or copy pages form this book there are no page numbers on the worksheets you give your students. There are page numbers at the beginning of each section, since they are only meant for the teacher. We put large headings with the name of the topic at the top of each page to make it easier for you to navigate through the book.

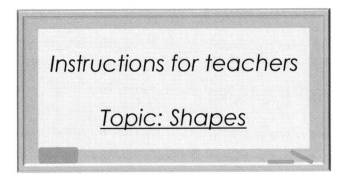

Instructions for teachers

Topic: Shapes

- ## Write the shape names

Students practice the names of the shapes and their penmanship by writing the names of the shapes on the lines.

- ## Color the shapes

Students color the robot by coloring the shapes according to the color guide at the bottom.

- ## Draw shapes on the kite tail

Students draw shapes on the kite tail and write what shapes they have drawn on the lines at the bottom.

- ## Draw and write what shape it is

Students look around and draw things from their environment that are a specific shape on the paper. They then write what shape it is on the line. For example, they might draw a clock and write "It is a circle".

Shapes

diamond

triangle

circle

crescent

semi-circle

star

square

rectangle

oval

Shapes

Color the shapes.

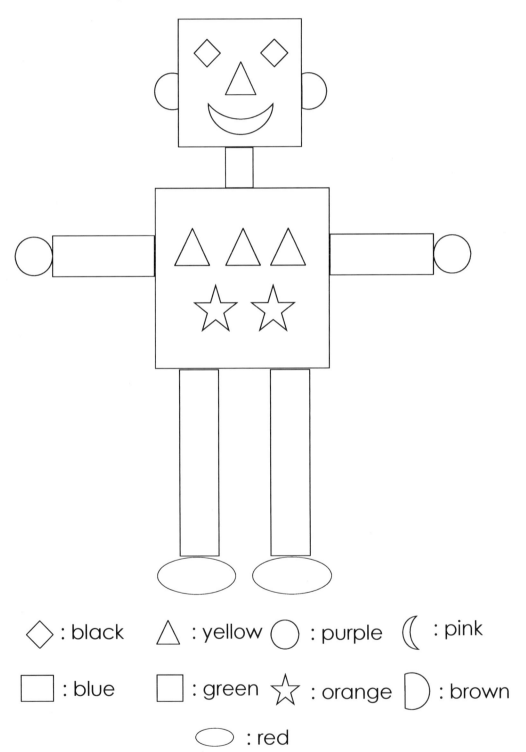

◇ : black   △ : yellow   ◯ : purple   ☽ : pink

▭ : blue   ▭ : green   ☆ : orange   ◗ : brown

⬭ : red

Shapes

Draw shapes on
your kite's tail.

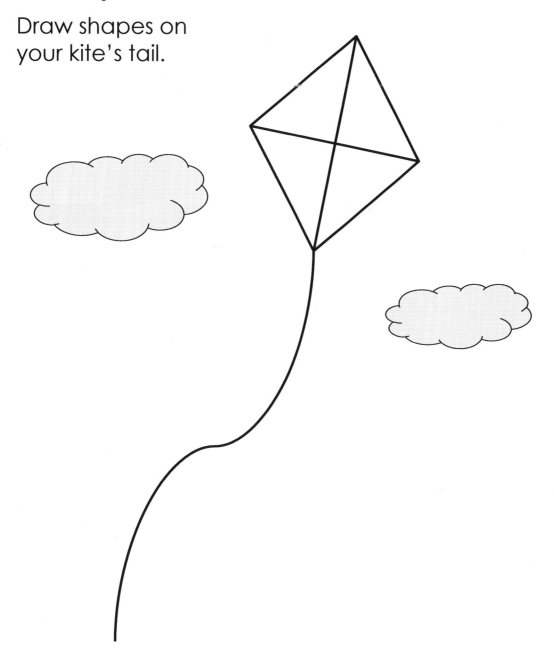

My kite's tail has _____ , _____ , _____ ,

and _____ .

Shapes

Draw things around you and write what shape it is.

It is a _____ .

It is a _____ .

_____ .

_____ .

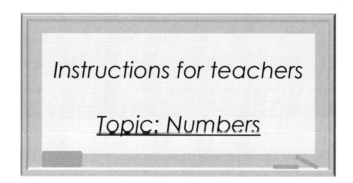

Instructions for teachers

Topic: Numbers

- # Bingo

Decide on a range of numbers (i.e. 1 – 25). Students write numbers within that range on the bingo sheet. The teacher then plays bingo with whatever variations they prefer. The bingo board can also be cut to form a smaller board.

What to prepare: Pieces of paper with numbers on them and a box or bag will be needed to play this game. (Alternatively, a random number generator on Google can save some preparation time.) A prize. (Giving out a prize makes the game more fun. Even if it is a small piece of candy.)

- # Lottery activity

Have students pick 4 numbers they like for A, B, and C. Then have them write their numbers inside the circles. Teachers need to limit the numbers (i.e. between 1 to 5 or 6 to 10). Whoever guesses the correct numbers will win. Guessing all 4 numbers correctly may take a lot of time, so teachers should limit how many numbers students need to get in order to win. Winners could also be chosen by correct numbers regardless of what order the numbers are in.

What to prepare: Same materials as bingo.

- # Listen and write the numbers (2 sheets)

Read out the numbers from the teacher's answer key and students write the correct numbers on their sheet. Elicit from the students what the numbers are.

- # Write about your numbers

Students draw themselves and then fill in the blanks with numbers that pertain to them.

11

Numbers

Bingo!

Numbers

2546- 8521450 - 58963320

Good luck!

Your numbers

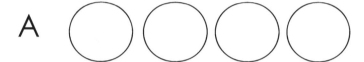

Numbers

Listen to your teacher and fill in the blanks.

Hello, my name is Tom.
I am _____ years old.

I live at _____ Wesley Rd.

My birthday is June _____th.

My phone number is
(_____)_____-_____.

Numbers

ANSWER KEY

Hello, my name is Tom. I am **8** years old.

I live at **1934** Wesley Rd.

My birthday is June **15th.**

My phone number is **(954)687-2310**.

Numbers

Draw your face and write about yourself.

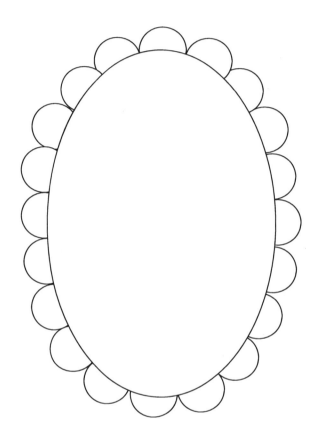

My name is _____ .

I am _____ years old.

I have _____ family members.

I have _____ brothers/sisters.

My favorite number is _____ .

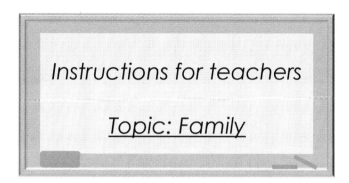

Instructions for teachers

Topic: Family

- ## Label the family members (2 sheets)

Students label the family members on the family tree. Alternatively they can write the names of their own family members.

There is one sheet for boys and one for girls.

The family member word bank at the bottom can be cut off to make it more challenging.

- ## Family member fill in the blanks

Students write the correct answers in the blanks using the family tree.

- ## Make your own family tree

Students make their own family tree by drawing their family members and putting in their names. There are lines at the bottom so that students can write about their family. (i.e. My cousin's name is Paul. My uncle is very nice. etc.)

Family

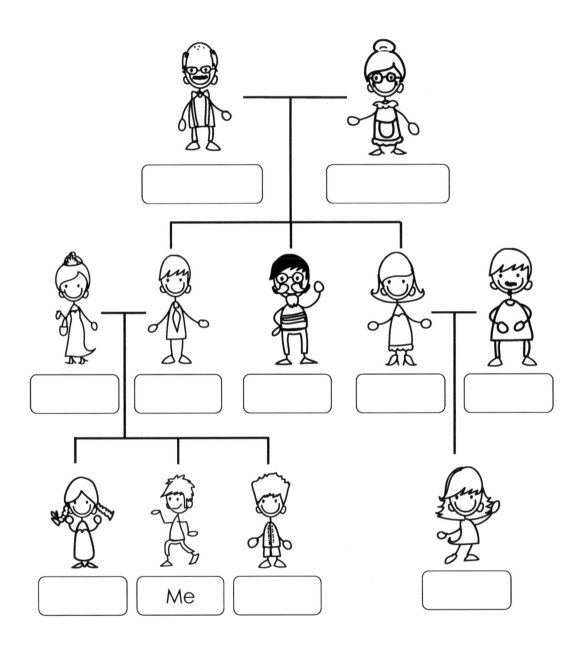

----

mother   uncle   cousin   brother   father

grandmother   sister   aunt   grandfather

Family

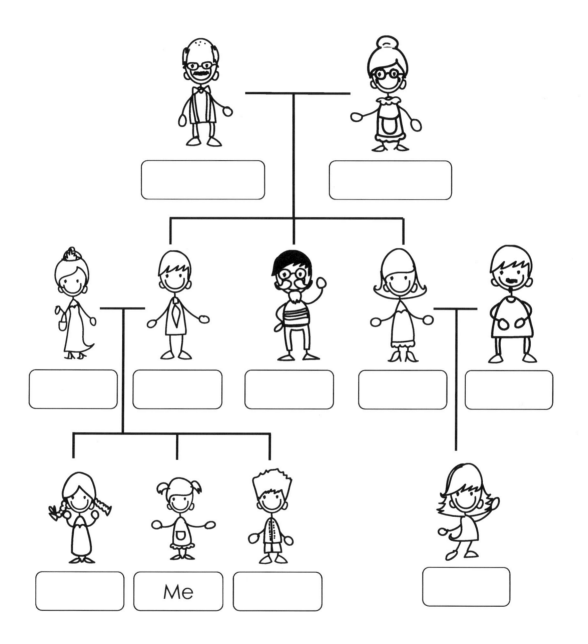

mother   uncle   cousin   brother   father

grandmother   sister   aunt   grandfather

Family

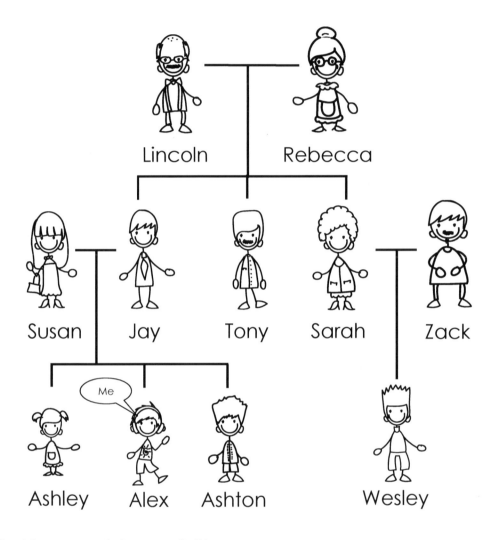

Lincoln Rebecca

Susan Jay Tony Sarah Zack

Ashley Alex Ashton Wesley

1. What is my cousin's name? It's _____ .

2. Who is my father's brother? It's _____. He's your _____ .

3. How many uncle's do I have? You have _____ uncles.

4. Who is my grandmother's daughter? It's _____ . She's your _____ .

5. What is my aunt's husband's name? It's _____ .

Family

Make your own family tree.

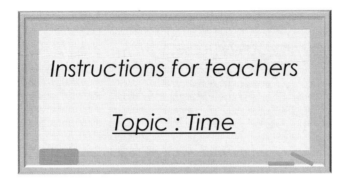

Instructions for teachers

Topic : Time

- # Make a clock
Students can cut out and make their own clocks. The teacher can then call out times and have students put the time on their clock.

The clock can be made to work in a number of ways. If the teacher laminates the clocks, blue tack can be used to hold the hands in place. Alternatively a push pin in the front which goes through to an eraser on the back can also work.

- # Snakes and Ladders
The clocks are empty so the teacher (or students) can customize the time. Students roll a die to move forward. When students land on a clock they must say the time. If they say it incorrectly they go back. Whoever gets to the finish box wins. Two students or a group of students can play this game.
What to prepare: A die (dice) and two coins (or board pieces) The board can also be enlarged when making copies for easier use.

- # What time do you...
Students draw the hands of the clock to show the proper time they do the activity. They then write the time on the line. For the last one they create their own example of when something is.

Time

minute hand

hour hand

Time

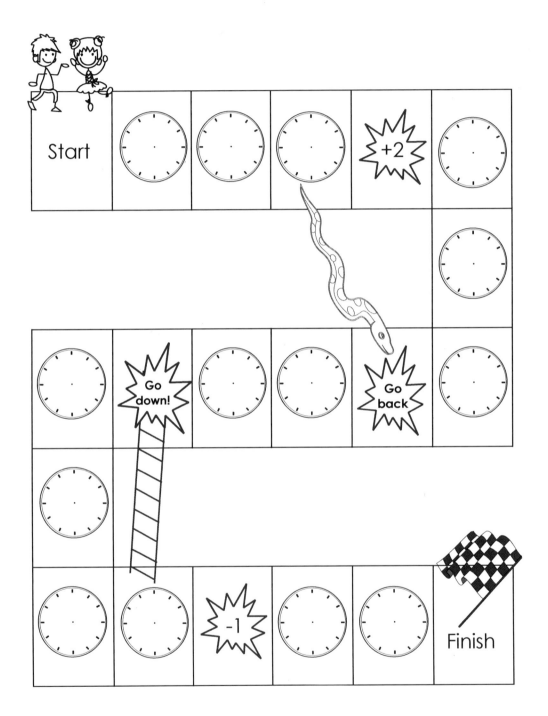

Time

What time is it?

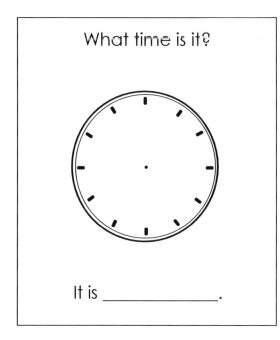

It is _____.

What time do you eat lunch?

I eat lunch at _____.

What time do you go to bed?

I go to bed at _____.

What time do you _____?

I _____.

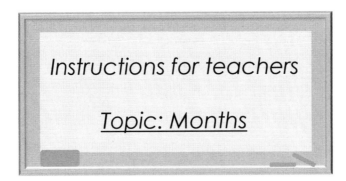

Instructions for teachers

Topic: Months

- ## Write the months (2 sheets)

Students practice the names of the months and their penmanship by writing the names of the months on the lines.

- ## Months word search puzzle (2 sheets)

Students find and circle the months in the puzzle. Some months are backwards.

A teacher's answer key is also included.

- ## What month...

Students write what month the event is in and create their own question. They can draw the event as well.

Months

January

February

March

April

May

June

July

Months

August

September

October

November

December

Months

J	M	A	F	T	S	U	G	U	A	W	S
M	A	P	N	O	V	E	M	B	E	R	E
A	Q	N	A	D	Y	L	U	J	U	E	P
R	S	A	U	G	U	S	J	O	L	B	T
C	E	M	A	A	C	H	U	P	I	M	E
H	A	N	P	J	R	Z	N	S	R	E	M
Y	B	A	I	C	K	Y	E	L	P	C	B
F	E	B	R	U	A	R	Y	I	A	E	E
R	E	P	O	C	T	O	B	E	R	D	R

January	July
February	August
March	September
April	October
May	November
June	December

Months

ANSWER KEY

				T	S	U	G	U	**A**		**S**
J											
M	A	**N**	O	V	E	M	B	E	R	E	
A	N			Y	L	U	**J**		E	P	
R	U				J		L	B	T		
C	**M**	A			U		I	M	E		
H	A		R		N		R	E	M		
Y			Y	E		P	C	B			
F	E	B	R	U	A	R	Y	Y	**A**	E	E
	O	C	T	O	B	E	R	**D**	R		

Months

What month is your
birthday?

It's in _____ .

What month is
Christmas?

It's in _____ .

What month does your
summer vacation start?

It starts in _____ .

_____
_____?

It's _____ .

Instructions for teachers

Topic: Days

- ## Write the days

Students practice the names of the days and their penmanship by writing the names of the days on the lines.

- ## What day...

Students write the correct day on the lines using the calendar.

- ## My days mini-book

Students write the day on the line at the top. Then they draw what happened during each day.

Creating the mini-book: Students or the teacher can cut out the mini book. Cut along the dotted lines. Make sure to cut the dotted lines in the middle but don't cut the solid lines in the middle. This will allow the book pages to be turned. Fold the book lengthwise and then fold it in accordion fashion like you were folding up a map.

Days

Sunday

Monday

Tuesday

Wednesday

Thursday

Friday

Saturday

Days

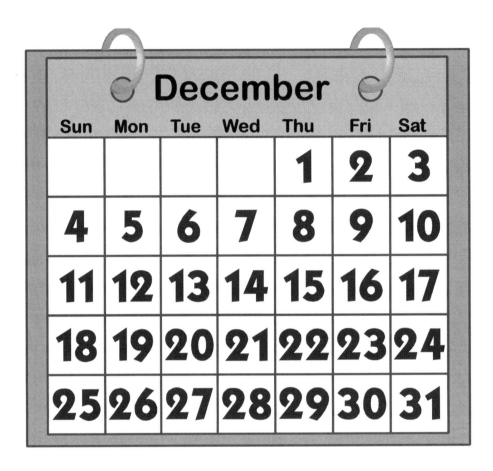

1. Today is 14th of December. What day is it?

    It is _____ .

2. What day was yesterday? *It was* _____ .

3. What day will it be tomorrow? *It will be* _____ .

4. What day is the last day of December?

    It is _____ .

5. What day is Christmas?   *It is* _____ .

Days

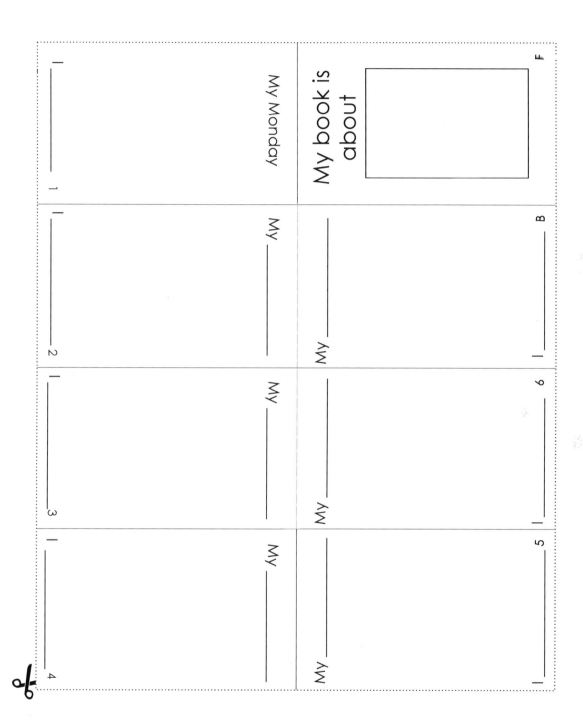

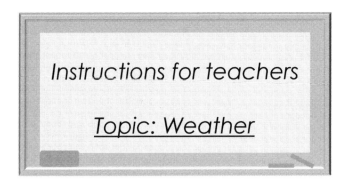

Instructions for teachers

Topic: Weather

- ## Write the weather

Students practice weather vocabulary and their penmanship by writing the types of weather on the lines.

- ## How's the weather?

Students use the weather report to write what the weather will be on the different days.

- ## Draw and write the weather

Students draw the weather to match the picture and write what the weather is on the line.

- ## Weather mini-book

Students draw the weather described at the top. For the last two they write the weather and then draw it.

Creating the mini-book: Students or the teacher can cut out the mini book. Cut along the dotted lines. Make sure to cut the dotted lines in the middle but don't cut the solid lines in the middle. This will allow the book pages to be turned. Fold the book lengthwise and then fold it in accordion fashion like you were folding up a map.

Weather

sunny

stormy

windy

rainy

cloudy

snowy

Weather

1. How's the weather on Thursday? It is _____ .

2. How's the weather on Saturday? _____ .

3. How's the weather on Tuesday? _____ .

4. Should I go on a picnic on Friday? *No, you shouldn't*
   because it will be _____ .

Weather

Look at the picture and draw the proper weather.

It is _____ .

It is _____ .

It is _____ .

It is _____ .

Weather

It is cloudy.

1

My book is
about

F

It is rainy.

2

Made by _____

B

It is stormy.

It is _____ .

3

6

It is windy.

It is _____ .

4

5

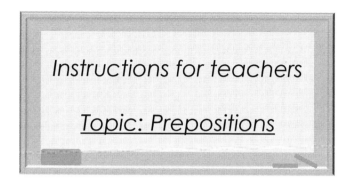

Instructions for teachers

Topic: Prepositions

- ## Match the picture and preposition

Students draw a line from the preposition to the picture.

- ## Fill in the prepositions

Students look at the picture and write the correct preposition in the blank. *The preposition word bank at the bottom can be cut off to make it more challenging. Some food and kitchen vocabulary may need to be taught before doing this and the following activity.*

- ## Preposition ask and answer game (4 sheets)

Two students pair up and have two different sheets, A and B. They can ask where the things are and listen to their partner's answer, then draw them on the paper. Their partner asks them where certain items are and they answer while their partner draws. They already have what they need to draw, but they don't have the location. *A teacher's answer key is included for both versions*

- ## Draw and write the prepositions

Students write and draw an object. Then they write where it is in relation to another object. (i.e. Where is the apple? It's on the table.) For two of the boxes, the students will need to write and draw two objects. Then write where they are in relation to each other using a preposition.

- ## Draw your room

Students draw their room and describe where things are located using prepositions.

Prepositions

Where is the apple? Draw a line.

1.  •   • in

2.  •   • under

3.  •   • on

4.  •   • between

5.  •   • above

6.  •   • next to

7.  •   • In front of

8.  •   • behind

Prepositions

1. The coffee cup is _____ the saucer.

2. The photo frame is _____ the microwave.

3. The tea pot is _____ the coffee cup and milk.

4. The plate is _____ the microwave.

5. The fan is _____ the table.

6. The apple is _____ the table.

7. Coffee is _____ the coffee cup.

8. The milk carton is _____ the microwave.

----

on   above   under   behind

next to   in front of   between   in

Prepositions

Ask and listen to your friend about where things are and draw them.

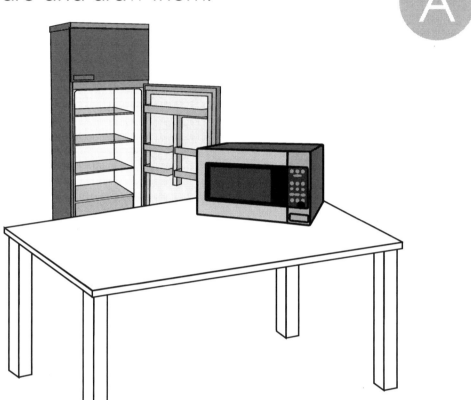

What you need to draw is..

The cheese is in the refrigerator.

The muffin is next to the microwave.

The plate is in front of the microwave.

The egg is on the plate.

The cat is under the table.

For your friend

Prepositions

ANSWER KEY

What you need to draw is..

The cheese is in the refrigerator.

The muffin is next to the microwave.

The plate is in front of the microwave.

The egg is on the plate.

The cat is under the table.

For your friend

Prepositions

Ask and listen to your friend about where things are and draw them.

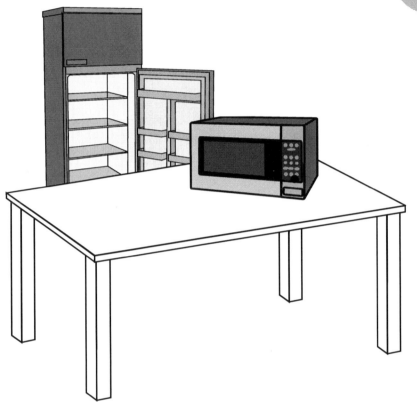

What you need to draw is..

The fan is above the microwave.

The hamburger is next to the microwave.

For your friend

The ice cream is in the refrigerator.

The plate is on the table and the pancakes are on the plate.

The slice of pizza is under the table.

Prepositions

ANSWER KEY

B

What you need to draw is..

The fan is above the microwave.

The hamburger is next to the microwave.

For your friend

The ice cream is in the refrigerator.

The plate is on the table and the pancakes are on the plate.

The slice of pizza is under the table.

Prepositions

Where is the _____ ?

It is _____ .

Where is the _____ ?

It is _____ .

Where is the _____ ?

It is _____ .

_____ ?

_____ .

Preposition

Draw your room and write where things are.

_____

_____

_____

_____

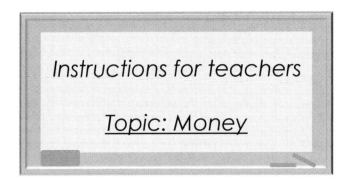

Instructions for teachers

Topic: Money

Note to teachers: This book uses U.S. money for the money section.

• Match the money

Students draw a line connecting the picture to the name of the coin and amount.

• How much is it?

Students add up the money and write the correct amount in the correct format on the line.

• Flea market (2 sheets)

Students buy things from the flea market. They can write what they are going to buy and add money on the line, or teachers can limit the amount of money students can spend. For example, students will have only 30$ to buy things from the flea market.

The worksheet with two stars has more complicated numbers.

• Online shopping

Students will pretend to shop online. Teachers can give students a shopping list or students can buy things freely. Students draw items and write a price.

Money

1.  •   •dime•   •1 cent

2.   •   •quarter•   •5 cents

3.  •   •nickel•   •10 cents

4.  •   •penny•   •25 cents

Money

How much is it?

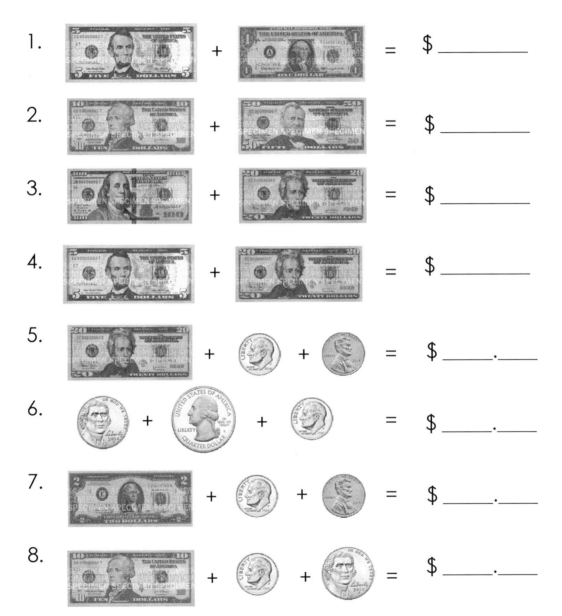

1.   +   = $ _____

2.   +   = $ _____

3.   +   = $ _____

4.   +   = $ _____

5.   +   +   = $ _____._____

6.   +   +   = $ _____._____

7.   +   +   = $ _____._____

8.   +   +   = $ _____._____

Money

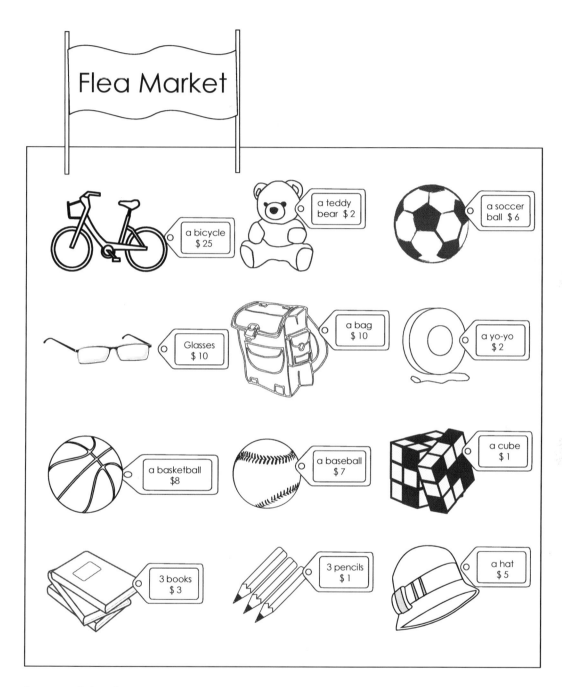

I want to buy _____

_____.

My total is $ _____ .

Money

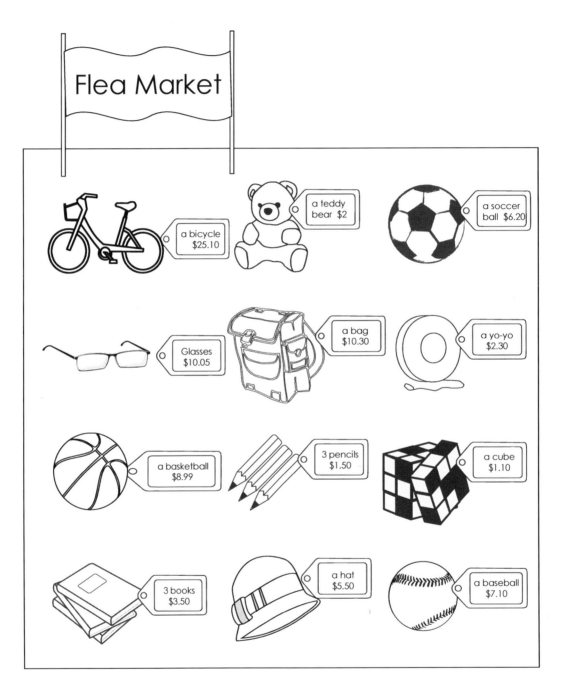

Flea Market

a bicycle $25.10

a teddy bear $2

a soccer ball $6.20

Glasses $10.05

a bag $10.30

a yo-yo $2.30

a basketball $8.99

3 pencils $1.50

a cube $1.10

3 books $3.50

a hat $5.50

a baseball $7.10

I want to buy _____

_____.

My total is $ _____ .

Money

🛒 Your cart

$ _____

$ _____

$ _____

$ _____

$ _____

$ _____

Order Total:

$ _____

____ items in your cart

$ _____

$ _____

Edit your cart

Check out

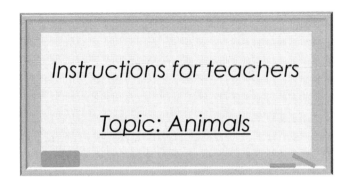

Instructions for teachers

Topic: Animals

- ## Write the animal name (3 sheets)

Students write the name of the animal under the picture.

If you aren't sure of an animal name, check the corresponding flash card in the resource section. More stars at the top right mean more difficult vocabulary. The stars are also used to match the vocabulary to the crossword puzzles.

- ## Animal crossword puzzles (6 sheets)

Students write the animal name in the correct spaces using the picture cue.

An answer key is included for each of the 3 puzzles.
The animal vocabulary at the bottom can be cut off to make it more challenging.
The stars on the top right indicate difficulty and vocabulary set.

- ## Extra animal vocabulary (2 sheets)

These animals are less commonly known and can be used as extra vocabulary.
Students fill in the blanks with the names of the animals.

- ## Match the animals to the letters

The students finish writing the animal name. The first letter is already given.

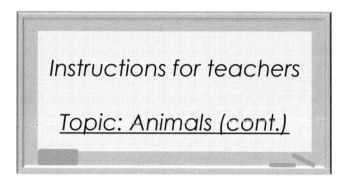

Instructions for teachers

Topic: Animals (cont.)

- ## Where do we live?

Students write the name of the animal and/or draw the animal in the place it belongs. Multiple correct answers are possible.

- ## Draw the animal faces (3 sheets)

Students draw the animal face and write what animal it is.

- ## Who am I? (3 sheets)

Students guess the correct animal based on the clues and write the animal name in the blank. Students also create their own clues and have other students guess the correct animal.

These are quite difficult and so might be better suited for more advanced students.

- ## My favorite animal

Students draw their favorite animal and write something about the animal or why it is their favorite.

Animals

_____   _____   _____

_____   _____   _____   _____

_____   _____   _____   _____

Animals

_____   _____   _____

_____   _____   _____

_____   _____   _____

_____   _____   _____

Animals

_____ _____ _____

_____ _____ _____

_____ _____ _____

_____ _____ _____

Animals

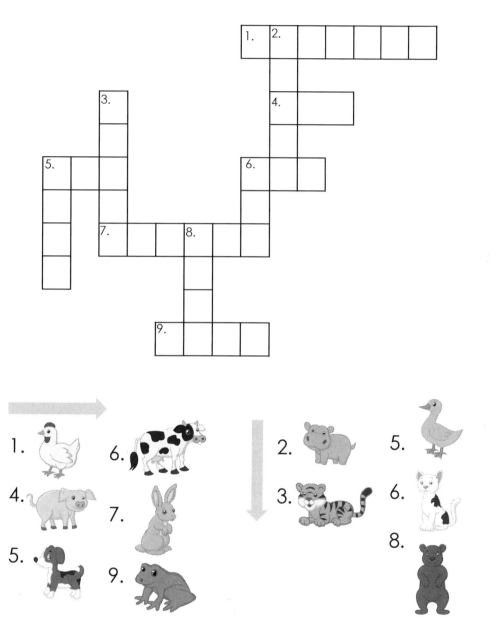

----

rabbit   duck   cow   tiger   hippo

pig   dog   cat   chicken   bear   frog

Animals

ANSWER KEY

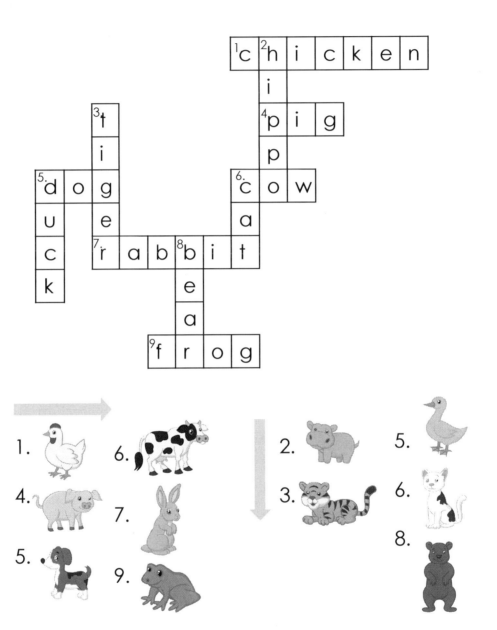

¹c	²h	i	c	k	e	n		

Crossword solution:

¹c ²h i c k e n
   i
   ⁴p i g
   p
³t   p
i   ⁶c o w
⁵d o g   a
u e
c ⁷r a b ⁸b i t
k   e
     a
    ⁹f r o g

1. chicken
6. cow
2. hippo
3. tiger
5. duck
6. cat
4. pig
7. rabbit
5. dog
8. bear
9. frog

---

rabbit   duck   cow   tiger   hippo

pig   dog   cat   chicken   bear   frog

Animals

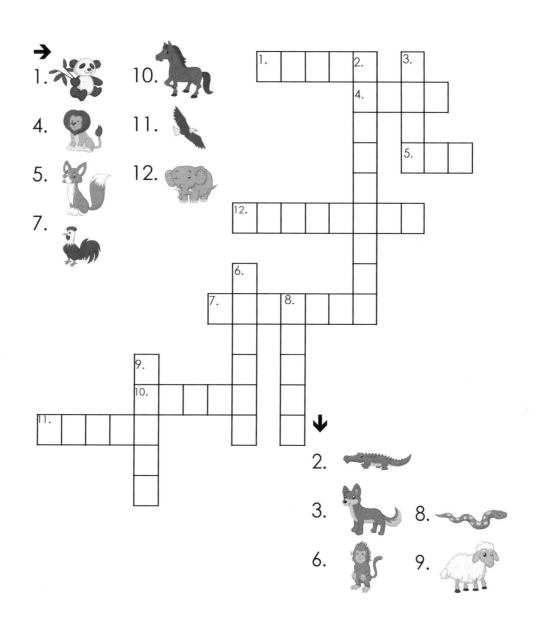

1.   10.

4. 11.

5. 12.

7.

2.

3. 8.

6. 9.

---

lion   wolf   rooster   alligator   elephant   snake

horse   monkey   sheep   panda   fox   eagle

Animals

ANSWER KEY

★ ★

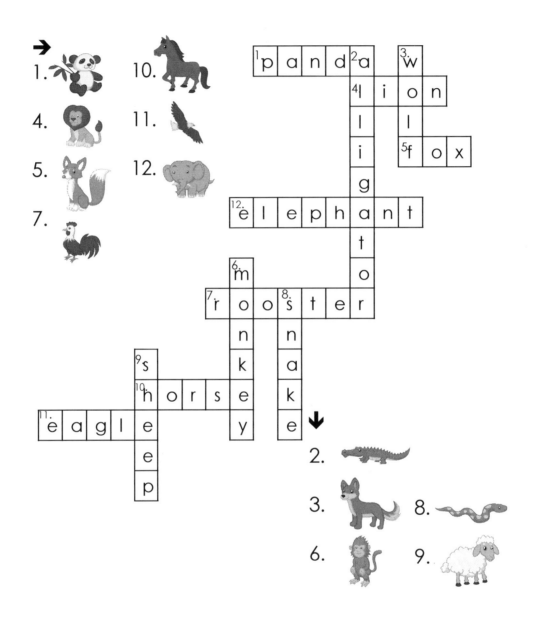

1. 4. 5. 7. 10. 11. 12.

Across / Down answers:

1. p a n d a
2. a
3. w
4. l i o n
5. f o x
6. m
7. r o o s t e r
8. s
9. s
10. h o r s e
11. e a g l e
12. e l e p h a n t

a l l i g a t o r

w o l f

m o n k e y

s n a k e

s h e e p

2. 3. 8. 6. 9.

Animals

----

parrot   camel   penguin   flamingo   giraffe   squirrel

whale   seal   skunk   ostrich   gorilla   bull   swan

Animals

ANSWER KEY

ANSWER KEY

Crossword grid:

```
              ¹f
  ²g o r i l l a
              a
      ³o      m        ⁴p
  ⁵c  ⁶s q u i r r e l        ⁷w
  ⁸p a r r o t    n     n      h      ⁹s
    m      r     g   ¹⁰g i r a f f e
    e      i     o     u      l      a
  ¹¹b u l l      c           i      e      l
          h          ¹²s k u n k
                     w
                     a
                     n
```

→

2. 10.
6. 11.
8. 12.

↓

1. 7.
3. 9.
4. 12.
5.

- -

parrot   camel   penguin   flamingo   giraffe   squirrel

whale   seal   skunk   ostrich   gorilla   bull   swan

Animals

_____ _____ _____

_____ _____ _____

_____ _____ _____

_____ _____ _____

Animals

Animals

Write the animals name for each letter.

A_____   G_____   R_____

B _____   H_____   S_____

C_____   K_____   T_____

D_____   L _____   W_____

E_____   M_____   Z_____

F_____   P_____

Animals

Write the name of the animal in the place they belong.

Farm animals

Zoo animals

Pet animals

Animals

Draw the animal faces.

It is a _____.

It is a _____.

It is a _____.

_____.

Animals

Draw the animal faces.

It is a _____ .

It is an _____ .

It is a _____ .

_____ .

Animals

Draw the animal faces.

It is a _____ .

It is a _____ .

It is a _____ .

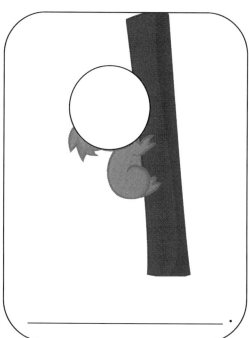

_____ .

Animals

Who am I?

I love to sleep a lot.

I always stay in a tree.

I am gray and white.

You can see me in

Australia.

It is a _____ .

I like to eat fish.

People think I don't

like dogs.

I like to be alone.

I am a pet.

It is a _____ .

I am green.

I can jump high.

I make lots of noise

when it rains.

It is a _____ .

_____

_____

_____

_____

_____

It is a/an _____ .

Animals

Who am I?

I have a long neck.

I like to eat leaves.

I am yellow with brown

spots.

It is a _____ .

I am very scary.

I might win if I fight a

lion.

I have orange and

black stripes.

It is a _____ .

_____

_____

_____

_____

It is a/an _____ .

_____

_____

_____

_____

It is a/an _____ .

Animals

Who am I?

I walk on two feet.

I can swim fast, but I walk slowly.

You can visit me at the South Pole.

It is a _____ .

_____

_____

_____

_____

_____

It is a/an _____ .

_____

_____

_____

_____

It is a/an _____ .

_____

_____

_____

_____

It is a/an _____ .

Animals

What is your favorite animal?

_____

_____ .

MINI-BOOK TEMPLATE AND FLASH CARDS

To make a mini-book:

Cut out the mini book. Cut along the dotted lines. Make sure to cut the dotted lines in the middle but don't cut the solid lines in the middle. This will allow the book pages to be turned. Fold the book lengthwise and then fold it in accordion fashion like you were folding up a map.

Flash cards:

All flash cards have the answers already on them. In order to quiz students, the answers can be folded back behind the card. Also, the cards can be folded together to make double sided flashcards.

Money:

The money can be cut out and used in class. *Also as a side note, the US quarter has many designs on the back. One design was chosen but you may want to let students know that real US quarters have many designs on the back. The front remains the same though.*

My book is
about

F

B

1

2

6

3

5

4

triangle

square

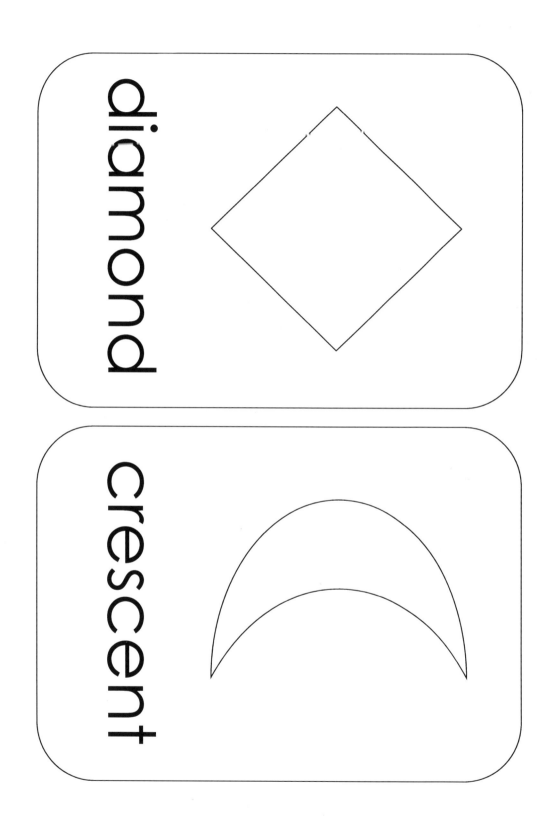

diamond

crescent

star

rectangle

circle

semi-circle

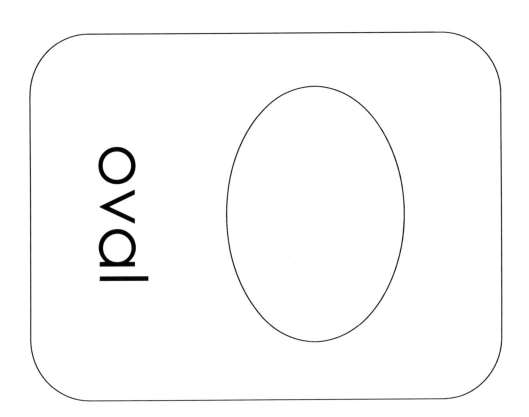

oval

snowy

sunny

rainy

stormy

cloudy

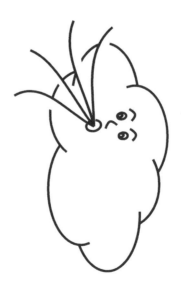

windy

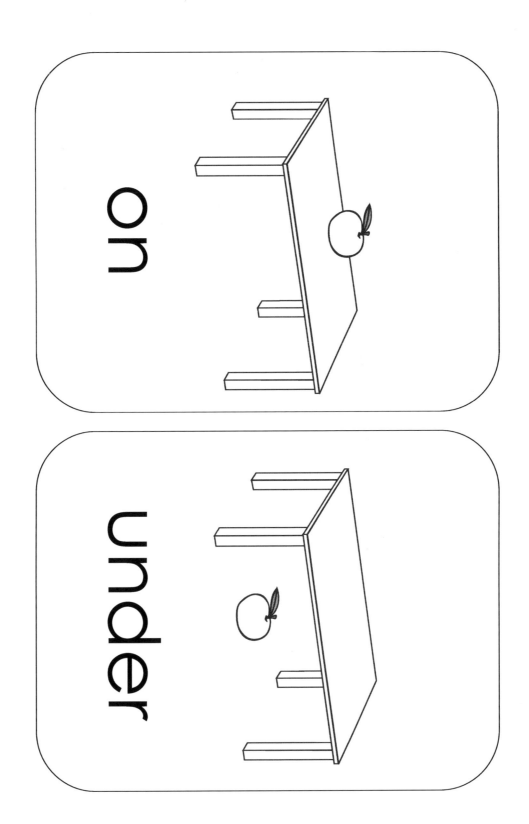

in

above

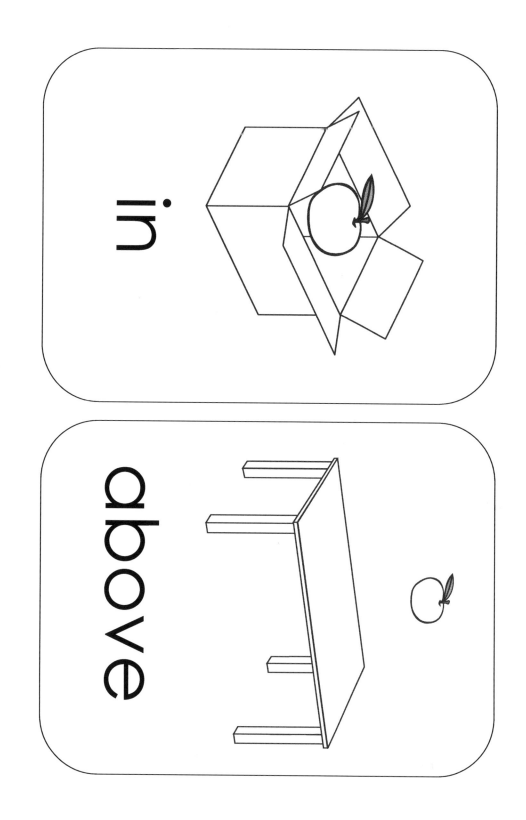

next to

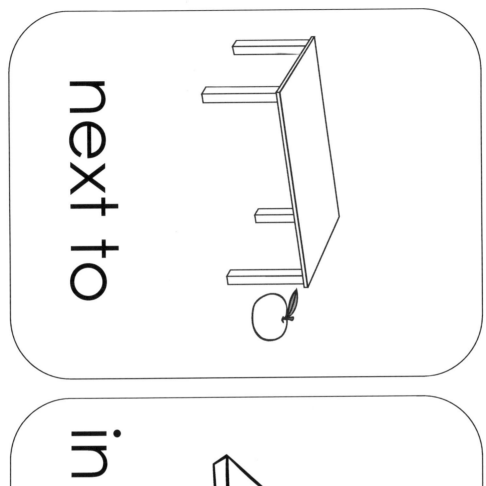

in front of

behind

between

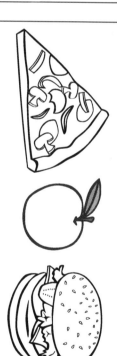

chicken

bear

dog

tiger

hippo

rabbit

cat

cow

pig

duck

frog

End of one star animals

elephant

monkey

fox

lion

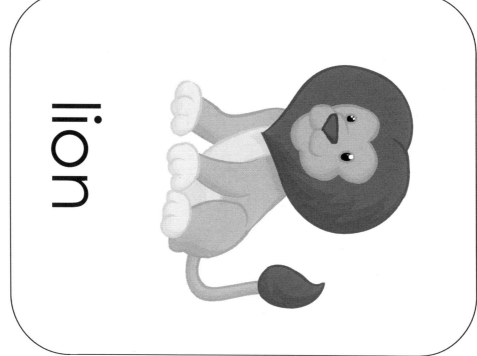

wolf

panda

horse

rooster

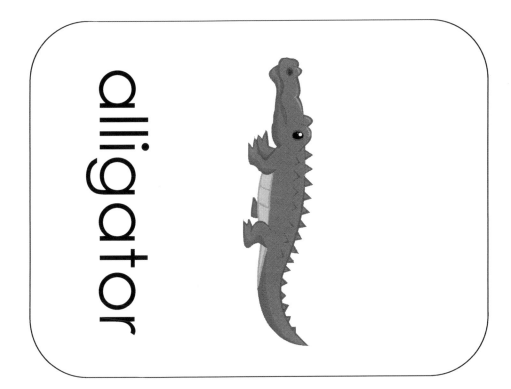

alligator

eagle

sheep

snake

whale

bull

camel

skunk

giraffe

gorilla

penguin

flamingo

seal

ostrich

parrot

squirrel

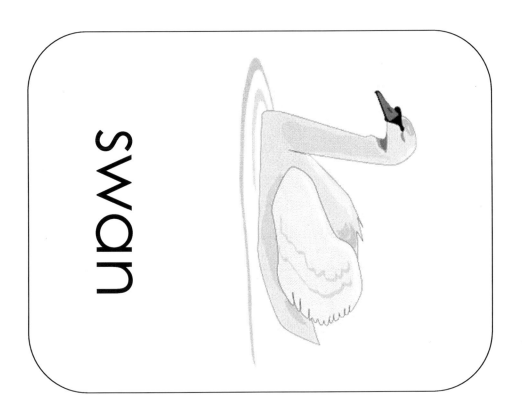

swan

End of two star animals

kangaroo

zebra

deer

rhino

boar

cheetah

bull

raccoon

sloth

goat

polar bear

moose

hedgehog

dolphin

turkey

toucan

koala

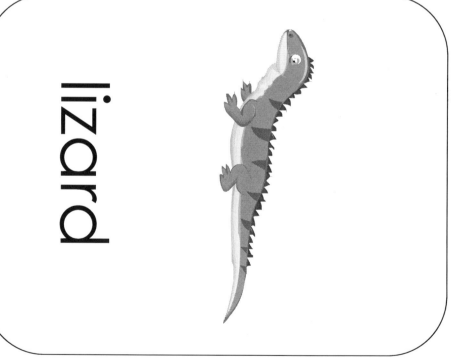

lizard

platypus

butterfly

beaver

anteater

shark

walrus

Enjoy the book?

We hope so!
I love hearing feed back! So if you have any comments or suggestions, or you just want to let me know how an activity went in your class, you can email me at:

miryung@eslconversationquestions.com

You can let others know about the book!
I would be very grateful if you would leave an honest review on Amazon. It helps other teachers find our books, which helps me make more books. Every review makes a huge difference!

Plus if you leave a review, you can join our review club and get free review copies of our new books and other books in our growing collection. You can find out more in the extras section at the beginning of the book.

Do you teach adults or IELTS?
Speaking of other books in our growing collection. If you teach adults you might want to check out our other books:

1,000 Conversation Questions: Designed for Use in the ESL or EFL Classroom

500 Grammar Based Conversation Questions

ESL Role Plays: 50 Engaging Role Plays for ESL and EFL Classes

We also have an IELTS book you can check out:

IELTS Study Guide: Quick Tips, Tricks, and Strategies

68842812R00073